Andrew Brodie Basics
LET'S DO SPELLING

FOR AGES 9-10

with over **100** reward stickers

- Over 400 words to practise and learn
- Regular progress tests
- Extra tips and brain booster questions

Published 2014 by Bloomsbury Publishing Plc
50 Bedford Square, London, WC1B 3DP

www.bloomsbury.com

ISBN 978-1-4729-0862-9

Copyright © 2014 Bloomsbury Publishing
Text copyright © 2014 Andrew Brodie
Cover and inside illustrations of Comma the Cat and Andrew Brodie © 2014 Nikalas Catlow
Other inside illustrations © 2014 Steve Evans

A CIP catalogue for this book is available from the British Library.

10 9 8 7 6 5 4 3 2 1

Printed in China by Leo Paper Products

This book is produced using paper that is made from wood grown in managed, sustainable forests. It is natural, renewable and recyclable. The logging and manufacturing process conform to the environmental regulations of the country of origin.

To see our full range of titles visit **www.bloomsbury.com**

BLOOMSBURY

Notes for parents

What's in this book

This is the fifth book in an exciting new series of *Andrew Brodie Basics: Let's Do Spelling*. Each book contains more than four hundred words especially chosen to boost children's confidence in spelling and to reflect the demands of the new National Curriculum.

By the end of Key Stage 2, most children are confident in the skills of 'segmenting' (breaking words down to spell them) and 'blending' (combining sounds together to read whole words) and will apply these skills when learning the spellings in this book. Of course, some words do not follow regular phonic patterns so your child will need to learn these 'tricky' words by looking at individual letters and the general shape of the word.

How you can help

To get the most out of this book, take the time to discuss the activities with your child when there are no distractions around and they are in a responsive and enthusiastic mood. Talk through each of the practice words and what they mean by using them in spoken sentences, or by asking your child to make up sentences containing the words. Putting up posters of useful words around the house, such as the days of the week and the months of the year, might also help with spelling generally.

To begin with, your child might find the spellings in this book quite tricky, but as they work their way through the activities and become familiar with the spelling patterns their confidence should grow. The level of difficulty is increased gradually throughout the book, but some spelling patterns are repeated to provide lots of opportunities for reinforcement and practice. Always be ready to provide plenty of encouragement and explain that they should learn from their mistakes rather than get disheartened.

Look out for...

Look, cover, write, check

Some pages feature 'Look, cover, write, check' exercises. Your child might have already come across this strategy in school. Ask your child to **look** carefully at each word, learning the shape of it and any letter patterns it contains. When they feel they know it, ask them to **cover** it with their hand or a piece of paper and to try writing it. They then look back at the original word and **write** it again to **check** that they really know it.

Comma the Cat

Look out for Comma the Cat who tells your child which words to focus on for the progress test at the end of each section. You could help your child to learn these words by posting them around the house on sticky notes or writing them on flashcards for quick memory games.

Brodie's Brain Boosters

Brodie's Brain Boosters feature quick extra activities designed to make your child think, using the skills and knowledge they already have. Some of these will ask your child to think of rhyming words. Don't worry if your child finds a rhyming word that doesn't match the spelling pattern of the given word. Use the opportunity to compare the spellings – looking carefully at words is, of course, the whole point of the activity!

The answer section

The answer section at the end of this book can also be a useful learning tool. Ask your child to compare their spellings with the correct spellings provided on the answer pages. If they have spelt the words correctly, congratulate them, but if they haven't, don't let them worry about it! Instead, encourage them to learn the correct versions. Give lots of praise for any success.

Singular and Plural

To change most words from singular to plural you just need to add an s, but for some words ending in y you need to replace the y with i before adding es to make them plural.

Make these singular words into plurals.

camera ➡ _____   city ➡ _____

lady ➡ _____   tarantula ➡ _____

umbrella ➡ _____   curry ➡ _____

party ➡ _____   pizza ➡ _____

koala ➡ _____   story ➡ _____

Choose words from above to fit into the sentences below.

Everybody had _____ because it was raining so hard.

I like adventure _____ .

I found a spider in the sink but it wasn't a _____ .

She smiled at the _____ , hoping that the photograph would come out well this time.

'Good evening, _____ and gentlemen!'.

I go to lots of birthday _____ .

I always have rice with my _____ .

Words Ending in 'f'

For some words ending in f, you need to replace the f with v then add es to make them plural. For example, the word thief is singular and the word thieves is plural.

Make these singular words into plurals.

thief ➡ _____ shelf ➡ _____

knife ➡ _____ hoof ➡ _____

leaf ➡ _____ half ➡ _____

loaf ➡ _____ calf ➡ _____

yourself ➡ _____ wolf ➡ _____

Choose words from above to complete the sentences below. Some of the words will be singular and some will be plural.

Put the _____ and forks on the table.

Please tidy the books on the _____.

Cut the cake into two _____.

The pack of _____ were running quickly through the forest.

Horses have metal shoes fastened to their _____.

We bought three _____ of bread to make all the sandwiches.

'Look after _____!' our grandparents said to us.

The police caught all the _____.

Comma says...
Learn these words for your first progress test.

knives   wolves

halves   loaves

4

Sort the Words

Some words are spelt in exactly the same way, whether they are singular or plural. Sort the words below into singular or plural.

Watch out! One of the words can have its plural spelt in two different ways!

cacti sheep geniuses ~~children~~ cactus mice genius

~~child~~ geese fungi deer genii teeth fungus

fish woman tooth mouse

women goose

Words that are spelt the same for singular and plural

Singular Words

child

Plural Words

children

Comma says...
Learn these words for your first progress test.

women

cactus

cacti fungi

Brodie's Brain Booster

Use these letters to make one word:
l o o a v c n
Clue: molten lava comes from this.

Prefix Practice

Some words start with the same prefix.

~~transport~~   ~~automobile~~   ~~telescope~~   translate   ~~bicentenary~~   autograph   bicycle

telepathy   telephone   transmit   bilingual   autobiography   transparent

biceps   television   transatlantic   transparency   automatic   telegraph   binoculars

Sort the words into prefix families.

Words starting with **auto**

automobile

Words starting with **bi**

bicentenary

Words starting with **tele**

telescope

Words starting with **trans**

transport

Comma says...

Learn these words for your first progress test.

automobile   **binoculars**

telescope   **transparent**

Brodie's Brain Booster

Use a dictionary to find out what the prefixes 'auto', 'tele', 'bi' and 'trans' mean.

Write the Words

Cover each word and see if you can write it without looking.
Then check and write it again.

LOOK (THEN COVER)	WRITE	CHECK
spaghetti		
macaroni		
kangaroo		
sauna		
fiesta		
bacteria		
echo		
radio		
potato		
volcano		

Choose words from above to complete the sentences below.

When I was travelling in Australia I saw a _____ hopping across a golf course.

There was a loud _____ in the cave.

How do you make crisps out of a _____ ?

I heard the song on the _____ .

Brodie's Brain Booster

Can you think of a word that rhymes with 'swimmer'?

Comma says...

Learn these words for your first progress test.

radio **bacteria** **spaghetti** **volcano**

Use the words you have been practising to fill the gaps.

1 The hairdressers was for men, _____ and children.

2 The _____ Mount Vesuvius destroyed the city of Pompeii.

3 Mushrooms and toadstools are types of _____ .

4 I have a very prickly _____ on my windowsill.

5 Lots of _____ are prickly.

6 Mum told me to cut the cake into two _____ .

7 I try to eat my _____ tidily but it slithers over my chin and makes a mess!

8 The programme on the _____ was very boring so we turned it off.

9 Yoghurt is made from milk fermented by _____ .

10 I like to eat poppadoms with _____ .

11 I closed my left eye and looked through the _____ with my right eye.

12 You use both eyes when looking through _____ .

13 I felt like a celebrity because there were so many _____ pointing at me!

14 I was very careful with the forks and spoons but I dropped all the _____ on the floor.

15 The _____ of bread smelt wonderful when they came out of the bakery.

16 Another name for a car is an _____ .

17 Glass is _____ so we can see through it.

18 A large pack of _____ roamed across the wilderness.

19 Cardiff and Swansea are _____ in Wales.

20 We ordered three 12-inch _____ .

Score ___/20

Sort the Words

Some words are made from the same root word.

beautiful   cheer   skilfully   ~~careful~~   skill   dread   useful

dreadfully   ~~carefully~~   colour   dreadful   skilful   cheerful   usefully

colourfully   beauty   use   colourful   cheerfully   ~~care~~   beautifully

Sort the words into groups. The first group has been done for you.

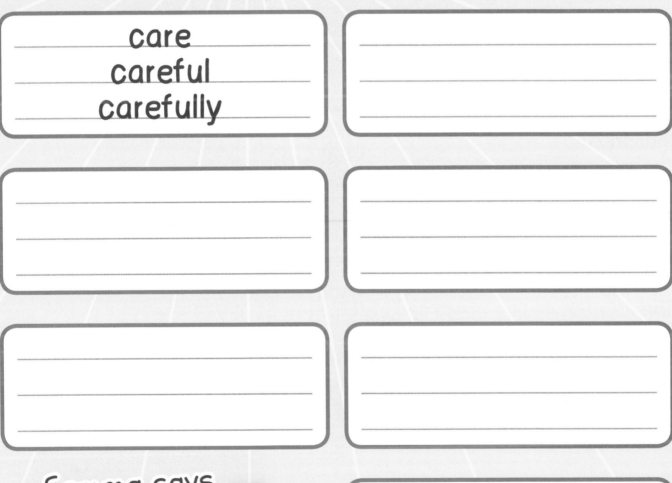

care
careful
carefully

Comma says...

Learn these words for your second progress test.

careful   colourful

carefully   beautifully

Write the Words

Cover each word and see if you can write it without looking. Then check and write it again.

LOOK (THEN COVER)	WRITE	CHECK
accompany		
bargain		
committee		
dictionary		
equipment		
forty		
guard		
individual		
leisure		
muscles		

Choose words from above to complete the sentences below.

The _____ watched over the jewels very carefully.

Since I've been going to the gym my _____ have grown.

Four tens make _____. 40

'Check the word in the _____,' said the teacher.

Comma says...
Learn these words for your second progress test.

committee
equipment
bargain
guard

Brodie's Brain Booster
Can you think of a word that rhymes with 'forty', but which is spelt differently?

Sort the Words

Read the words below.

confusion vision decision occasion extension mansion

television conclusion position pollution contribution collision

dilution distribution explosion expedition repetition lotion

condition competition

Copy the words on to the correct list.

WORDS ENDING WITH sion

_____

_____

_____

_____

_____

_____

_____

_____

Brodie's
Brain Booster
Can you think of a word that is an extension of the word 'invade' and ends with 'sion'?

WORDS ENDING WITH tion

_____

_____

_____

_____

_____

_____

_____

_____

_____

Comma says...
Learn these words for your second progress test.

pollution occasion

competition explosion

11

Alphabetical Order

Read the words below. Sometimes we need to look at the second or third letter of words to work out alphabetical order.

brother | centre | mosquito | children | description | loiter

earth | propose | extra | definite | important | donor

fields | lottery | worries | money | window | prepare | clothes

abseil | control | doctor | imitate | balloon | friends | abbreviate

Write the words in alphabetical order.

Comma says...

Learn these words for your second progress test.

description **imitate** **definite**

abbreviate

12

Write the Words

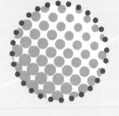

Cover each word and see if you can write it without looking.
Then check and write it again.

LOOK (THEN COVER)	WRITE	CHECK
guessed		
guest		
heard		
herd		
led		
lead		
aloud		
allowed		
past		
passed		

Choose words from above to complete the sentences below.

She was a _____ at the wedding.

I am not _____ to go out late at night.

We _____ the shops on the way to the sports centre.

The gutter was made of _____ .

Mum _____ that we had organised a surprise party for her.

Brodie's Brain Booster

Can you think of a word that rhymes with 'past'?

Use the words you have been practising to fill the gaps.

1 'Are we _____ to go out to play?'

2 The _____ decided that the school should have some new play equipment.

3 There was a loud _____ at the quarry.

4 'Colour the map _____' said the teacher.

5 The bride was dressed _____.

6 Some birds can _____ the sounds they hear.

7 The woman was a _____ at the hotel.

8 The archery instructor brought all the _____ we needed.

9 I _____ the answer to the question.

10 The costume was bright and _____.

11 The book was reduced to a _____ price.

12 The victim of the theft gave the police a clear _____ of the robber.

13 There was a _____ protecting the entrance to the palace.

14 Sometimes I prefer to read in my head but sometimes I have to read _____.

15 She gave a _____ answer to the question.

16 Over sixty people entered the _____.

17 _____ is very bad for the environment.

18 'Be _____ when you work out this question,' said the teacher.

19 'I'll let you off on this _____,' said the headteacher.

20 'How do you _____ the words 'will not'?' asked the teacher.

Score _____ /20

Sort the Words

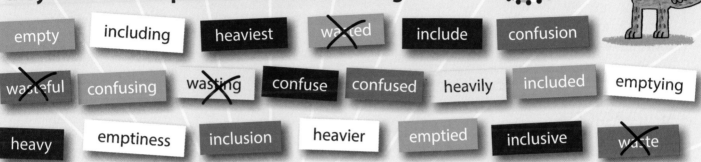

Some words are related to each other because they have similar parts or similar meanings.

empty · including · heaviest · ~~wasted~~ · include · confusion

~~wasteful~~ · confusing · ~~wasting~~ · confuse · confused · heavily · included · emptying

heavy · emptiness · inclusion · heavier · emptied · inclusive · ~~waste~~

Copy the words on to the correct list. One group has been done for you.

waste
wasting
wasted
wasteful

Comma says...

Learn these words for your third progress test.

including · confusion

wasteful · emptiness

15

Practise the Words

Cover each word and see if you can write it without looking.
Then check and write it again.

LOOK (THEN COVER)	WRITE	CHECK
jewellery		
explanatory		
voluntary		
factory		
literacy		
library		
definitely		
miserable		
literature		
interested		

Choose words from above to complete the sentences below.

'Are you _____ in science?' asked the teacher.

The cars are produced in a huge _____.

The celebrity was wearing lots of gold _____.

At school, we usually do _____ in the morning.

Brodie's Brain Booster

Can you think of a word that means the opposite of 'voluntary'?

Comma says...

Learn these words for your third progress test.

jewellery

library

voluntary

interested

16

Pair the Words

Read the words below. Sort them into pairs where one word is the root word and the other word is an extended version of the root word. The first pair has been for you.

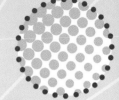

~~proper~~ inactive inconvenient convenient impolite illogical mature

polite attentive immature regular patient inattentive

accurate irregular impatient inaccurate logical active ~~improper~~

proper improper	

Comma says...
Learn these words for your third progress test.

mature impolite

inconvenient

irregular

Alphabetical Order

Read the words below. Sometimes you need to look at the
second or third letter of a word to work out alphabetical order.

builder   legislate   politician   benefactor   laminate   abstract

annual   removal   lemonade   yellowing   pollution   recorder

inflation   view   renovation   impression   beautician   business   disease

restore   durable   value   directory   vegetable   yesterday   yearning

Write the words in alphabetical order.

Write the Words

Always use your best handwriting!
Dogs are hopeless at handwriting.

Cover each word and see if you can write it
without looking. Then check and write it again.

LOOK (THEN COVER)	WRITE	CHECK
cinema		
decide		
cereal		
cylinder		
celebrate		
celebrating		
celebration		
celebrity		
December		
circulate		
circulation		
circuit		
certify		
certificate		
mercy		
merciful		
mercifully		
merciless		
mercilessly		
circumstances		

Comma says...

Learn these words for
your third progress test.

circulation

celebration

circumstances

cinema

Brodie's Brain Booster

Use these letters to make one word:
n o e a c
Clue: The Pacific, the Atlantic and the
Indian are all examples of these.

19

Use the words you have been practising to fill the gaps.

1 The opposite of fullness is _____ .

2 She wore too much expensive _____ .

3 'It's not very _____ to call people names,' said the headteacher.

4 My grandmother does _____ work in a charity shop.

5 My sister studies the heart and the _____ system of the body.

6 People can borrow books from the _____ .

7 The telephone rang when we were eating so it was very _____ .

8 I am very _____ in wildlife.

9 It is _____ to stare at people.

10 A hexagon can be regular or _____ .

11 The _____ was arguing with the interviewer on the News.

12 'Mind your own _____ !' the girl shouted when I asked her how she was.

13 Some people, _____ me, eat too much chocolate!

14 There was a lot of _____ when we started learning long division.

15 My _____ have changed so I can go to see the film after all.

16 The film is showing at the new _____ .

17 There was a big _____ when we won the game.

18 The girl's nails were sparkling after the _____ painted them.

19 It is very _____ not to use all of the paper.

20 The _____ did a great job on the extension.

Sort the Words

Dogs don't even know what suffixes and prefixes are!

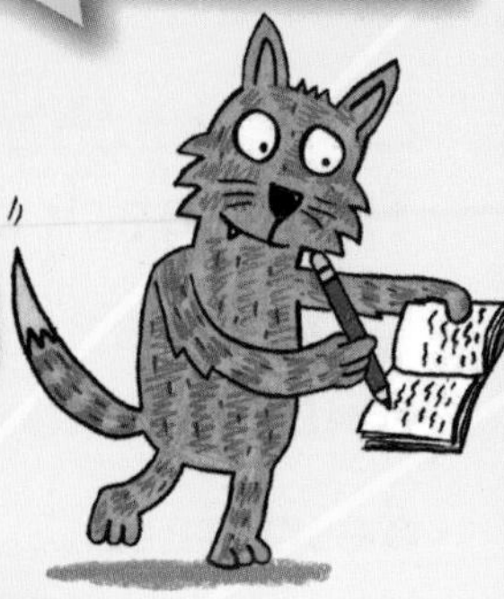

Some words are made from the same root word.

interest | relevance | irrelevantly | illegally | illegible

illegibly | miserably | legally | uninteresting | legal

interesting | legibly | relevantly | disinterest | relevant

miserable | illegal | irrelevant | legible | misery

Sort the words into groups. The first group has been done for you.

miserable
miserably
misery

Comma says...

Learn these words for your fourth progress test.

miserable **illegally** **uninteresting** **relevant**

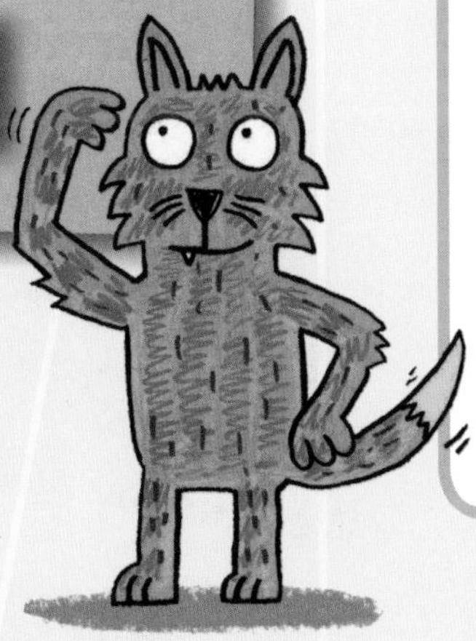

Tricky Words

Cover each word and see if you can write it without looking.
Then check and write it again.

LOOK (THEN COVER)	WRITE	CHECK
desperate		
generous		
marvellous		
Wednesday		
familiar		
family		
generally		
separate		
separately		
boundary		

Choose words from above to complete the sentences below.

The day after Tuesday is _____.

We ran to the far _____ of the field.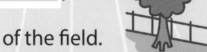

My sister was _____ to see me through the window.

'You two had better sit _____!' said the teacher.

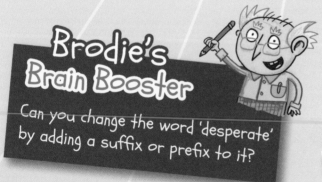

Brodie's Brain Booster

Can you change the word 'desperate' by adding a suffix or prefix to it?

Comma says...

Learn these words for your fourth progress test.

desperate   familiar

Wednesday

separate

22

Pair the Words

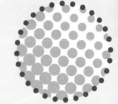

Read the words below. Sort them into pairs where one word is the root word and the other word is an extended version of the root word. The first pair has been done for you.

innocently anxiously ~~adorable~~ re-enter observe thorough notice

thoroughly enjoyment anxious enjoy horribly ~~adore~~ horrible

reasonable enter innocent noticeable observant reason

adore adorable	

Comma says...

Learn these words for your fourth progress test.

noticeable innocently

observant

anxiously

Alphabetical Order

Read the words below. Sometimes you need to look at the second or third letter of a word to work out alphabetical order.

entrance realise generous observe autumn imperial

national annual naughty fantastic interrupt garage original

obtuse favourite imagination absence narrow release restore

gradual familiar expedition fabulous exhibition ordinary

Write the words in alphabetical order.

Comma says... Learn these words for your fourth progress test.

absence interrupt

national

restore

Write the Words

Always use your best handwriting!

Cover each word and see if you can write it without looking.
Then check and write it again.

LOOK (THEN COVER)	WRITE	CHECK
carry		
carried		
carrying		
carrier		
reply		
replying		
replied		
replies		
difference		
different		
differently		
origin		
original		
originally		
company		
companion		
fright		
frighten		
frightened		
frightening		

Comma says...

Learn these words for your fourth progress test.

frightening **differently**

original **carried**

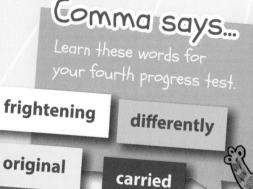

Brodie's Brain Booster

Use these letters to make one word:
r e t p a n
Clue: Your mum or dad is one of these.

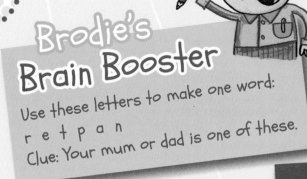

25

Progress Test 4

1. In the film the monster was very _____.

2. The day before Thursday is _____.

3. It's good to be cheerful, not _____.

4. We _____ all our things down to the beach.

5. 'Look at the picture carefully. You need to be very _____,' said the teacher.

6. When she won the gold medal, everyone sang the _____ anthem.

7. The driver seemed to be very _____ with the route.

8. 'Your idea for your story is very _____,' smiled the teacher.

9. The car was parked _____ so the police took it away.

10. After tearing up the paper, the boy acted _____.

11. The teacher made a note of the boy's _____.

12. She looked under the bed _____ in case there was a spider.

13. 'Why don't you try working out the question _____,' suggested the teacher.

14. 'There's been a _____ improvement in the behaviour of the children,' said the headteacher.

15. Look for all the _____ information before you try to answer the question.

16. I was disappointed because I found the exhibition very _____

17. There were _____ rooms for art and science.

18. I am so thirsty, I am _____ for a drink.

19. The building was falling down so we had to _____ it.

20. It's rude to _____ people when they are talking.

Score ___/20

26

Sort the Words

Remember that some words are made by adding suffixes or prefixes to a root word.

~~multiply~~   additional   ~~subtract~~   adding

~~add~~   multiple   undivided   ~~divide~~   subtracting

subtraction   subtracted   division   multiplying   addition   dividing

multiplied   multiplication   divided   added   additionally

Can you sort the words into groups?

subtract

add

multiply

divide

27

Practise the Words

Cover each word and see if you can write it without looking.
Then check and write it again.

LOOK (THEN COVER)	WRITE	CHECK
doctor		
inspector		
reactor		
actor		
conductor		
glacier		
either		
neither		
carpenter		
gardener		

Choose words from above to complete the sentences below.

The _____ visited the school to talk about the inspection.

We visited a _____ in the mountains of Switzerland.

My brother asked if I would like the chocolate or the toffee and I said that I didn't mind _____ of them.

I went to the _____ because I kept having stomach aches.

Comma says...

Learn these words for your fifth progress test.

inspector

conductor

either

glacier

Brodie's Brain Booster

Can you write a word related to the word 'carpenter'?

28

Pair the Words

Read the words below. Sort them into pairs where one word is the root word and the other word is an extended version of the root word. The first pair has been done for you.

proper ✗   different   attentively   politely   immature   impatient   actively

differently   conveniently   immaturely   generally   convenient   general

impatiently   attentive   active   properly ✗   polite   accurately   accurate

proper properly	

Alphabetical Order

Read the words below. Sometimes you need to look at the second or third letter of a word to work out alphabetical order.

massive   foolish   computer   warbling   colourful   museum   wishful

career   excellent   positive   wandering   prediction   shiny

exterior   fascinate   cosmetic   calculator   wondering   material   fortunate

persuade   shave   exact   should   condensation   sure

Write the words in alphabetical order.

Write the Words

Cover each word and see if you can write it without looking. Then check and write it again.

LOOK (THEN COVER)	WRITE	CHECK
electric		
electricity		
electrical		
electrician		
magic		
magical		
magically		
magician		
music		
musical		
musically		
musician		
politics		
political		
politically		
politician		
optic		
optical		
optically		
optician		

Comma says...

Learn these words for your fifth progress test.

electricity   optician

magical   political

Brodie's Brain Booster

Can you think of a word that rhymes with 'magic'?

Progress Test 5

Use the words you have been practising to fill the gaps.

1. The headteacher asked the parents for their _____ attention.

2. Visiting the castle was a _____ experience.

3. Twelve is a _____ of six.

4. There are several _____ parties in the British parliament.

5. The teacher said my work was _____ .

6. The _____ checked my eyes carefully.

7. The bus _____ stopped right outside my door.

8. I made a _____ that I would win the race but I came second.

9. The solar panels produce a lot of _____ on a sunny day.

10. The teacher asked for _____ information when my parents said I needed a day off.

11. We have to work as _____ as possible when we do maths questions.

12. We visited a _____ and were amazed by the flow of ice down the valley.

13. 'Can you tell me the way to the station?' asked the man _____ .

14. The girl was _____ by the horse.

15. I paced up and down, waiting _____ for the bus.

16. I made a mistake when I _____ four hundred and sixty-five from one thousand.

17. The _____ was delighted by the performance of his orchestra.

18. 'You can choose _____ of the two toys,' said Mum to the toddler.

19. The ticket _____ checked everybody's tickets.

20. The wallpaper in the toddler's room was very _____ .

Score ____ /20

32

Sort the Words

Remember that some words are made by adding suffixes or prefixes to a root word.

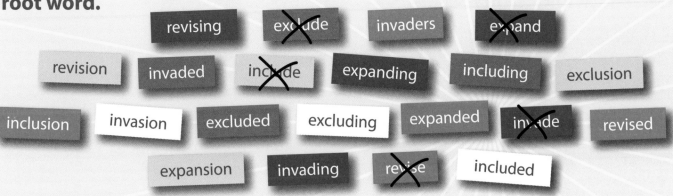

revising ~~exclude~~ invaders ~~expand~~

revision invaded ~~include~~ expanding including exclusion

inclusion invasion excluded excluding expanded ~~invade~~ revised

expansion invading ~~revise~~ included

Can you sort the words into groups?

invade	expand

revise	exclude

	include

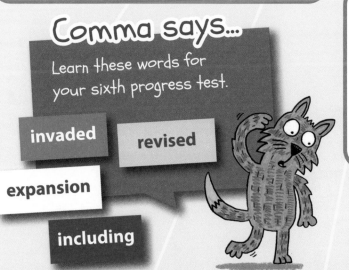

Comma says...

Learn these words for your sixth progress test.

invaded   revised

expansion

including

Practise the Words

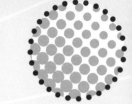

Cover each word and see if you can write it without looking.
Then check and write it again.

LOOK (THEN COVER)	WRITE	CHECK
proceed		
process		
propel		
produce		
productive		
production		
suspended		
suspect		
suspicious		
suspicion		

Choose words from above to complete the sentences below.

The police officer thought that the man's behaviour was very _____

We are doing three plays in our school _____ this year.

The projector is _____ from the ceiling.

I _____ that my teacher is planning a surprise for the end of term.

Brodie's Brain Booster
Can you change the word 'suspicious' by adding a suffix to it?

Match the Homophones

Words that sound the same but have a different meaning are called homophones. Match each one to its homophone pair. One has been done for you.

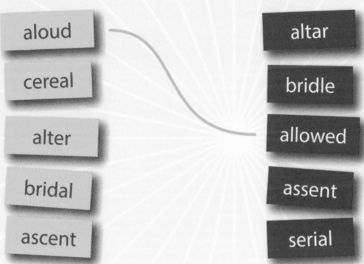

aloud		altar
cereal		bridle
alter		allowed
bridal		assent
ascent		serial

Choose words from above to complete the sentences below.

The headteacher gave his _____ to the planned trip.

The _____ car was decorated with white ribbons.

I always have _____ for breakfast.

The _____ of the mountain took several days.

I like reading to myself but I also like reading _____.

We put the _____ on the horse very carefully.

The _____ is a table at the front of a church.

Brodie's Brain Booster

Use these letters to make a word that sounds quite like 'desert' but is the name for a sweet course of a meal: s e d s t r e

Alphabetical Order

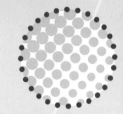

Read the words on the list. Sometimes you need to look at the second letter of a word to work out alphabetical order.

whistle following confession wrist canister suitable

shoulder earlobe estimation thigh steering eyebrow

nostril cautious wireless noticeable community forehead throat

stomach tongue fossil fault nervous elbow narrowly

Write the words in alphabetical order.

_____

_____

_____

_____

_____

_____

_____

_____

_____

_____

_____

_____

_____

_____

_____

_____

_____

_____

_____

_____

_____

_____

_____

_____

_____

Comma says...

Learn these words for your sixth progress test.

stomach   cautious

tongue   noticeable

36

Write the Words

Cover each word and see if you can write it without looking.
Then check and write it again.

LOOK (THEN COVER)	WRITE	CHECK
promotion		
devotion		
completion		
deletion		
possible		
possibly		
impossible		
possibility		
impossibility		
kind		
unkind		
unkindly		
kindness		
compose		
composer		
decompose		
composition		
probable		
improbable		
probably		

Comma says...

Learn these words for your sixth progress test.

probably   impossibility

decompose   kindness

Brodie's Brain Booster

Can you spell the plural of 'possibility'?

Use the words you have been practising to fill the gaps.

1 The football pitch was _____ by excited fans.

2 After I had eaten too much dessert I developed a _____ ache.

3 I am _____ going to have some chocolate later.

4 Everybody, _____ me, was really excited about the party.

5 All the vegetable peelings _____ in the compost bin.

6 The driver showed great _____ by allowing us to cross the road.

7 We should always be _____ before approaching a strange dog.

8 The doctor asked me to open my mouth and show her my _____ .

9 Mum was very _____ when a strange man came to the door, but it was no problem as he was delivering a parcel.

10 On special occasions I am _____ to stay up late.

11 I like to read _____ so that I can use lots of expression.

12 I know all my spellings because I have _____ them.

13 Railway tracks have gaps in them to allow for _____ in hot weather.

14 The first _____ of Mount Everest took place in 1953.

15 Lots of energy is used in the _____ of electricity.

16 Travelling to the sun is an absolute _____ .

17 There has been a _____ improvement in my spelling.

18 My favourite television _____ is broadcast every Saturday evening.

19 The growth of an oak tree is a very slow _____ .

20 Once we had reached the half-way point we immediately had to _____ to the next stage in the race.

Score _____ /20

Sort the Words

All the words below have double s.

~~possession~~ impressing aggressor confessing aggressive
confessor ~~aggression~~ possessor ~~confess~~ ~~obsessive~~
impressed possess ~~impression~~ possessing impress
confession impressive obsession confessed possessed

Can you sort the words into groups?

obsessive

impression

aggression

confess

possession

Comma says...

Learn these words for your seventh progress test.

aggressive confession possession

impressive

Write the Words

Cover each word and see if you can write it without looking.
Then check and write it again.

LOOK (THEN COVER)	WRITE	CHECK
depression		
percussion		
mission		
passionate		
procession		
profession		
professor		
replace		
replaceable		
irreplaceable		

Choose words from above to complete the sentences below.

Dad said not to worry because everything is _____ .

Mum said that wasn't true because some antiques are _____ .

Mum loves antiques, she is _____ about them.

I would like to play _____ instruments like really loud drums!

Brodie's Brain Booster

Can you change the word 'dangerous' by adding a suffix to it?

Comma says...

Learn these words for your seventh progress test.

mission	procession
professor	replace

Pair the Words

Read the words below and then join each one to its pair.
The first one has been done for you.

terrible	incredible
visible	officially
credible	partial
sensible	visibly
official	specially
special	essentially
artificial	confidentially
part	terribly
confidential	artificially
essential	sensibly

Comma says...
Learn these words for your seventh progress test.

visible   sensible

incredible   artificial

Brodie's Brain Booster
Can you add a prefix to the word 'visible' to make it into another word?

Alphabetical Order

Read the words below. Sometimes you need to look at the second or third letter of a word to work out alphabetical order.

sharing · tangling · figured · snipping · practical · gloomier

variation · trimmed · infiltration · prefer · flipped · shopping

gradual · visitor · swimming · filtered · taught · pretty · troubled

flopped · infection · presume · valuation · invitation · glacier · inflation

Write the words in alphabetical order.

_____ _____ _____

_____ _____ _____

_____ _____ _____

_____ _____ _____

_____ _____ _____

_____ _____ _____

_____ _____ _____

_____

_____

_____

_____

Comma says...

Learn these words for your seventh progress test.

invitation   practical

visitor   troubled

42

Write the Words

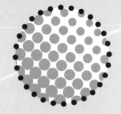

Cover each word and see if you can write it without looking.
Then check and write it again.

LOOK (THEN COVER)	WRITE	CHECK
refer		
referring		
referred		
referral		
reference		
referee		
prefer		
preference		
preferring		
preferred		
transfer		
transference		
transferring		
transferred		
coordinate		
coordinated		
coordinating		
coordination		
coordinator		
uncoordinated		

Comma says...

Learn these words for your seventh progress test.

preference
referee
uncoordinated
transferred

Brodie's Brain Booster

Can you write the plural of 'autobiography'?

43

Use the words you have been practising to fill the gaps.

1 The headteacher told the boy not to be so _____ .

2 Young children are often _____ when they first begin to play with bats and balls but they improve with practice.

3 The performance of the players was very _____ .

4 The _____ blew the whistle for the end of the match.

5 We had a _____ to our house last night.

6 The _____ is brilliant at maths.

7 My friend's picture was absolutely _____ .

8 There was a long _____ of animals going into the ark.

9 My sister made a _____ to my mum that she had drunk all the milk.

10 She had to go to the shop to buy some milk to _____ what she had drunk.

11 The flowers looked real but they were _____ .

12 I gave my friend an _____ to my party.

13 Try not to be _____ by difficult maths.

14 My favourite _____ is my mobile phone.

15 Some people are very good at _____ activities such as woodwork.

16 'Try to be more _____ !' said the headteacher to the naughty boy.

17 The football player was _____ to a different team.

18 Do you have a _____ where we go for coffee?

19 The magic disappearing cat suddenly became _____ !

20 The last Apollo moon _____ took place in 1972.

Score _____ /20

ANSWERS

Page 3 • Singular and Plural

cameras	cities
ladies	tarantulas
umbrellas	curries
parties	pizzas
koalas	stories

umbrellas
stories
tarantula
camera
ladies
parties
curries

Page 4 • Words Ending in 'f'

thieves	shelves
knives	hooves
leaves	halves
loaves	calves
yourselves	wolves

knives
shelves
halves
wolves
hooves
loaves
yourselves
thieves

Page 5 • Sort the Words

Upper ring contains:
mouse goose child woman
fungus cactus tooth

Overlap contains:
fish sheep deer

Lower ring contains:
mice geese children women
fungi cacti teeth geniuses genii

Brain Booster:
volcano

Page 6 • Prefix Practice

Words starting with 'auto':
automatic
automobile
autograph
autobiography

Words starting with 'bi':
bilingual
bicentenary
biceps
binoculars
bicycle

Words starting with 'tele':
telepathy
telephone
television
telegraph
telescope

Words starting with 'trans':
transport
transmit
transparent
transparency
transatlantic
translate

Page 7 • Write the Words

words written as neatly as possible

kangaroo
echo
potato
radio

Brain Booster:
dimmer, trimmer, slimmer or any other rhyming word

Page 8 • Progress Test 1

1. women	11. telescope
2. volcano	12. binoculars
3. fungi	13. cameras
4. cactus	14. knives
5. cacti	15. loaves
6. halves	16. automobile
7. spaghetti	17. transparent
8. television	18. wolves
9. bacteria	19. cities
10. curries	20. pizzas

Page 9 • Sort the Words

dread	colour
dreadful	colourful
dreadfully	colourfully
cheer	beauty
cheerful	beautiful
cheerfully	beautifully
skill	use
skilful	useful
skilfully	usefully

Page 10 • Write the Words

words written as neatly as possible

guard
muscles
forty
dictionary

Brain Booster:
naughty or any other rhyming word

Page 11 • Sort the Words

Words ending with 'sion':
mansion
explosion
occasion
conclusion
extension
confusion
decision
collision
television
vision

Words ending with 'tion':
dilution
pollution
contribution
distribution
expedition
repetition
position
condition
competition
lotion

Brain Booster:
invasion

45

Page 12 • Alphabetical Order

abbreviate	extra
abseil	fields
balloon	friends
brother	imitate
centre	important
children	loiter
clothes	lottery
control	money
definite	mosquito
description	prepare
doctor	propose
donor	window
earth	worries

Page 13 • Write the Words

words written as neatly as possible

guest
allowed
passed
lead
guessed

Brain Booster:
last, fast, cast, or any other rhyming word

Page 14 • Progress Test 2

1. allowed	11. bargain
2. committee	12. description
3. explosion	13. guard
4. carefully	14. aloud
5. beautifully	15. definite
6. imitate	16. competition
7. guest	17. pollution
8. equipment	18. careful
9. guessed	19. occasion
10. colourful	20. abbreviate

Page 15 • Sort the Words

include	confuse
including	confusing
include	confused
inclusion	confusion
inclusive	

heavy
heavier
heavily
heaviest

empty
emptiness
emptied
emptying

Page 16 • Practise the Words

words written as neatly as possible

interested
factory
jewellery
literacy

Brain Booster:
involuntary, compulsory, or any other appropriate word

Page 17 • Pair the Words

proper, improper
mature, immature
patient, impatient
polite, impolite
attentive, inattentive
convenient, inconvenient
accurate, inaccurate
active, inactive
logical, illogical
regular, irregular

Brain Booster:
irrelevant, relevance, or relevantly

Page 18 • Alphabetical Order

abstract	lemonade
annual	politician
beautician	pollution
benefactor	recorder
builder	removal
business	renovation
directory	restore
disease	value
durable	vegetable
impression	view
inflation	yearning
laminate	yellowing
legislate	yesterday

Page 19 • Write the Words

words written as neatly as possible

Brain Booster:
ocean

Page 20 • Progress Test 3

1. emptiness	11. politician
2. jewellery	12. business
3. mature	13. including
4. voluntary	14. confusion
5. circulation	15. circumstances
6. library	16. cinema
7. inconvenient	17. celebration
8. interested	18. beautician
9. impolite	19. wasteful
10. irregular	20. builder

Page 21 • Sort the Words

legal	interest
legally	interesting
illegal	disinterest
illegally	uninteresting
legible	relevant
legibly	relevance
illegible	relevantly
illegibly	irrelevant
	irrelevantly

Page 22 • Tricky Words

Wednesday	desperate
boundary	separately

Brain Booster:
desperately, desperation, or any other appropriate word

Page 23 • Pair the Words

adore, adorable
notice, noticeable
enjoy, enjoyment
observe, observant
innocent, innocently
thorough, thoroughly
reason, reasonable
horrible, horribly
anxious, anxiously
enter, re-enter

Brain Booster:
roughly, roughness, roughen,
or any other appropriate word

Page 24 • Alphabetical Order

absence	imagination
annual	imperial
autumn	interrupt
entrance	narrow
exhibition	national
expedition	naughty
fabulous	observe
familiar	obtuse
fantastic	ordinary
favourite	original
garage	realise
generous	release
gradual	restore

Page 25 • Write the Words

words written as neatly as
possible

Brain Booster:
fraction

Page 26 • Progress Test 4

1.	frightening	11.	absence
2.	Wednesday	12.	anxiously
3.	miserable	13.	differently
4.	carried	14.	noticeable
5.	observant	15.	relevant
6.	national	16.	uninteresting
7.	familiar	17.	separate
8.	original	18.	desperate
9.	illegally	19.	restore
10.	innocently	20.	interrupt

Page 27 • Sort the Words1

subtract	add
subtracting	adding
subtracted	added
subtraction	addition
	additional
multiply	additionally
multiplying	
multiplied	divide
multiple	dividing
multiplication	divided
	undivided
	division

Page 28 • Practise the Words

words written as neatly as
possible

inspector
glacier
either
doctor

Brain Booster:
carpentry, or any other
appropriate word

Page 29 • Pair the Words

proper, properly
immature, immaturely
impatient, impatiently
polite, politely
attentive, attentively
convenient, conveniently
accurate, accurately
active, actively
different, differently
general, generally

Brain Booster:
activity, activation, or any other
appropriate word

Page 30 • Alphabetical Order

calculator	material
career	museum
colourful	persuade
computer	positive
condensation	prediction
cosmetic	shave
exact	shiny
excellent	should
exterior	sure
fascinate	wandering
foolish	warbling
fortunate	wishful
massive	wondering

Page 31 • Write the Words

words written as neatly as
possible

Brain Booster:
tragic or any other rhyming word

Page 32 • Progress Test 5

1.	undivided	11.	accurately
2.	magical	12.	glacier
3.	multiple	13.	politely
4.	political	14.	fascinated
5.	excellent	15.	impatiently
6.	optician	16.	subtracted
7.	conveniently	17.	conductor
8.	prediction	18.	either
9.	electricity	19.	inspector
10.	additional	20.	colourful

Page 33 • Sort the Words

invade	expand
invaders	expanded
invading	expanding
invaded	expansion
invasion	
	exclude
revise	excluded
revised	excluding
revising	exclusion
revision	
	include
	included
	including
	inclusion

Page 34 • Practise the Words

words written as neatly as possible

suspicious
production
suspended
suspect

Brain Booster:
suspiciously

Page 35 • Match the Homophones

aloud, allowed
cereal, serial
alter, altar
bridal, bridle
ascent, assent

Brain Booster:
dessert

Page 36 • Alphabetical Order

canister	nervous
cautious	nostril
community	noticeable
confession	shoulder
earlobe	steering
elbow	stomach
estimation	suitable
eyebrow	thigh
fault	throat
following	tongue
forehead	whistle
fossil	wireless
narrowly	wrist

Page 37 • Write the Words

words written as neatly as possible

Brain Booster:
possibilities

Page 38 • Progress Test 6

1. invaded
2. stomach
3. probably
4. including
5. decompose
6. kindness
7. cautious
8. tongue
9. suspicious
10. allowed
11. aloud
12. revised
13. expansion
14. ascent
15. production
16. impossibility
17. noticeable
18. serial
19. process
20. proceed

Page 39 • Sort the Words

obsessive
obsession

impression
impress
impressing
impressed
impressive

aggression
aggressive
aggressor

confess
confessor
confessing
confessed
confession

possession
possess
possessor
possessing
possessed

Page 40 • Write the Words

replaceable
irreplaceable
passionate
percussion

Brain Booster:
replacement

Page 41 • Pair the Words

terrible, terribly
visible, visibly
credible, incredible
sensible, sensibly
official, officially
special, specially
artificial, artificially
part, partial
confidential, confidentially
essential, essentially

Brain Booster:
invisible

Page 42 • Alphabetical Order

figured	presume
filtered	pretty
flipped	sharing
flopped	shopping
glacier	snipping
gloomier	swimming
gradual	tangling
infection	taught
infiltration	trimmed
inflation	troubled
invitation	valuation
practical	variation
prefer	visitor

Brain Booster:
practically or practicality

Page 43 • Write the Words

words written as neatly as possible

Brain Booster:
autobiographies

Page 44 • Progress Test 7

1. aggressive
2. uncoordinated
3. impressive
4. referee
5. visitor
6. professor
7. incredible
8. procession
9. confession
10. replace
11. artificial
12. invitation
13. troubled
14. possession
15. practical
16. sensible
17. transferred
18. preference
19. visible
20. mission

Well done!
See you next time.